Course | Corequisite Workbook for College Algebra
Course Number | **MATH 012**
ROWAN COLLEGE AT BURLINGTON COUNTY

http://create.mheducation.com

Copyright 2018 by McGraw-Hill Education. All rights
reserved. Printed in the United States of America. Except as
permitted under the United States Copyright Act of 1976, no part
of this publication may be reproduced or distributed in any form
or by any means, or stored in a database or retrieval system,
without prior written permission of the publisher.

This McGraw-Hill Create text may include materials submitted to
McGraw-Hill for publication by the instructor of this course.
The instructor is solely responsible for the editorial content of such
materials. Instructors retain copyright of these additional materials.

ISBN-10: 1308570082   ISBN-13: 9781308570082

Contents

Credits

Polynomial and Rational Functions 35

Exponential and Logarithmic Functions 51

Systems of Equations and Inequalities 67

Matrices and Determinants and Applications 83

Equations and Inequalities

Prerequisite Review Linear Equations and Rational Equations   Section 1.1

This worksheet will cover the following:
Objective 1: Properties and Real Numbers and Simplifying Expressions
Objective 2: Multiplication of Polynomials/Special Case Products: Perfect Square Trinomial
Objective 3: Factoring Trinomials by the AC-Method
Objective 4: Least Common Denominator (LCD)

Objective 1: Properties and Real Numbers and Simplifying Expressions
Simplify by clearing parentheses and combining *like* terms.

1. $-3(2t+4w)+8(2t-4w)$

3. $\dfrac{1}{5}(15-4p)-\dfrac{1}{10}(10p+5)$

2. $6(x+3y)-(6x-5y)$

4. $8k-4(k-1)+7-k$

Objective 2: Multiplication of Polynomials/Special Case Products: Perfect Square Trinomial
Square the binomials.

5. $(a+5)^2$ 6. $(a-3)^2$ 7. $(3+4q)^2$

Objective 3: Factoring Trinomials by the AC-Method
Factor the trinomials using the AC-method.

8. $3x^2+13x+4$ 10. $6n^2+7n-3$

9. $2p^2-3p-2$ 11. $4w^2-9w+2$

Prerequisite Review Linear Equations and Rational Equations   Section 1.1

Objective 4: Least Common Denominator (LCD)
Identify the least common denominator.

12. $\dfrac{7}{12}; \dfrac{1}{18}$

13. $\dfrac{5}{6a^2b}; \dfrac{a}{12b}$

14. $\dfrac{6}{(w+3)(w-8)}; \dfrac{w}{(w-8)(w+1)}$

15. $\dfrac{r}{10r+5}; \dfrac{2}{16r+8}$

16. $\dfrac{2}{x-3}; \dfrac{x+1}{x^2+4x-21}$

Prerequisite Review Applications with Linear and Rational Equations   **Section 1.2**

This worksheet will cover the following:
Objective 1: Translations Involving Linear Expressions
Objective 2: Translations Involving Proportions

Objective 1: Translations Involving Linear Expressions
Write an expression representing the unknown quantity.

1. In a math class, the number of students who received an "A" in the class was 5 more than the number of students who received a "B." If x represents the number of "B" students, write an expression for the number of "A" students.

2. There are 5,682,080 fewer men on Facebook than women. If x represents the number of women using Facebook, write an expression for the number of men using Facebook.

3. There are 10 times as many Facebook users as there are Twitter users. If x represents the number of Twitter users, write an expression for the number of Facebook users.

4. Stacey downloaded twice as many songs as William. If x represents the number of songs downloaded by William, write an expression for the number downloaded by Stacey.

5. Emily made $20 less than three times Stephen's weekly salary. If x represents Stephen's weekly salary, write an expression for Emily's weekly salary.

6. This year's senior class has 117 fewer students than last year's class. If x represents the number of students in last year's class, write an expression for the number of students in this year's senior class.

Objective 2: Translations Involving Proportions
Translate the following into equations involving proportions. Do not solve.

7. Toni drives her Honda Civic 132 miles on the highway on 4 gallons of gas. At this rate how many miles can she drive on 9 gallons of gas?

Prerequisite Review Applications with Linear and Rational Equations   **Section 1.2**

8. Tim takes his pulse for 10 seconds and counts 12 beats. How many beats per minute is this?

Prerequisite Review   **Complex Numbers**   **Section 1.3**

This worksheet will cover the following:
Objective 1: Simplifying Radicals by Using the Multiplication Property of Radicals
Objective 2: Multiplication Property of Radicals/Special Case Products
Objective 3: Rationalizing the Denominator

Objective 1: Simplifying Radicals by Using the Multiplication Property of Radicals
Simplify the radicals.

1. $\sqrt{63}$

2. $\sqrt{20}$

3. $\sqrt{50}$

4. $5\sqrt{18}$

5. $2\sqrt{24}$

6. $\sqrt{80}$

7. $-6\sqrt{75}$

8. $\dfrac{2\sqrt{27}}{3}$

9. $\dfrac{7\sqrt{24}}{2}$

Objective 2: Multiplication Property of Radicals/Special Case Products
Multiply the radical expression.

10. $\left(y+\sqrt{6}\right)\left(y-\sqrt{6}\right)$

11. $\left(\sqrt{3}+x\right)\left(\sqrt{3}-x\right)$

Objective 3: Rationalizing the Denominator
For the following, rationalize the denominator.

12. $-\dfrac{1}{\sqrt{7}}$

13. $\dfrac{6}{\sqrt{8}}$

14. $\dfrac{2}{\sqrt{48}}$

15. $\dfrac{4}{\sqrt{2}+3}$

16. $\dfrac{6}{4-\sqrt{3}}$

Prerequisite Review   **Quadratic Equations**   **Section 1.4**

This worksheet will cover the following:
Objective 1: Special Case Products: Perfect Square Trinomials
Objective 2: Factoring Perfect Square Trinomials
Objective 3: Factoring Trinomials by the AC-Method
Objective 4: Division by a Monomial

Objective 1: Special Case Products: Perfect Square Trinomials
Multiply the binomials.

1. $(x-8)(x-8)$ 2. $(y+3)(y+3)$

Objective 2: Factoring Perfect Square Trinomials
Factor the polynomials.

3. $x^2 - 16x + 64$ 6. $3t^2 + 18t + 27$

4. $y^2 + 6y + 9$ 7. $25m^2 - 30mn + 9n^2$

5. $2a^2 - 20a + 50$

Objective 3: Factoring Trinomials by the AC-Method
Factor the trinomial.

8. $9h^2 - 3h - 2$

Objective 4: Division by a Monomial
Simplify the expressions.

9. $\dfrac{20 - 2\sqrt{3}}{4}$ 11. $\dfrac{9 + 4\sqrt{3}}{3}$

10. $\dfrac{49 - 35\sqrt{2}}{7}$

Prerequisite Review   Applications of Quadratic Equations   Section 1.5

This worksheet will cover the following:
Objective 1: Area of a Rectangle
Objective 2: Volume
Objective 3: Pythagorean Theorem
Objective 4: Area of a Triangle

Objective 1: Area of a Rectangle
1. Find the area of a rectangle that measures $3\,cm$ by $11\,cm$.

2. Find the area of a rectangle that measures $21\,ft$ by $5\frac{2}{3}\,ft$.

3. Find the area of the rectangle.

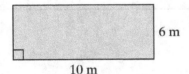

6 m

10 m

Objective 2: Volume
4. Find the volume of a rectangular solid that measures $5\,in$ by $4\,in$ by $9\,in$.

5. Find the volume of a rectangular solid that measures $6\frac{1}{2}\,in$ by $3\,in$ by $8\,in$.

6. Find the volume of the rectangular solid.

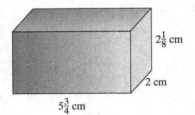

$2\frac{1}{8}$ cm

2 cm

$5\frac{3}{4}$ cm

Objective 3: Pythagorean Theorem
Find the length of the missing side.

Prerequisite Review   **Applications of Quadratic Equations**   **Section 1.5**

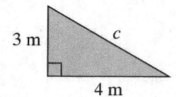

7.

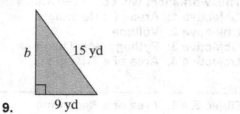

9.

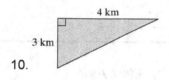

8.

Objective 4: Area of a Triangle
Find the area of the triangle.

10.

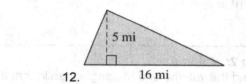

12.

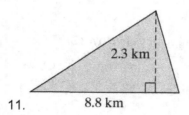

11.

Prerequisite Review   More Equations and Applications   Section 1.6

This worksheet will cover the following:
Objective 1: Factoring by Grouping
Objective 2: Restricted Values of a Rational Expression
Objective 3: Least Common Denominator
Objective 4: Definition of $a^{\frac{1}{n}}$ and $a^{\frac{m}{n}}$
Objective 5: Converting Between Rational Exponents and Radical Notation

Objective 1: Factoring by Grouping
Factor the following by grouping.

1. $8a^2 - 4ab + 6ac - 3bc$

3. $5a^2 + 30a - 2a - 12$

2. $xy - xz + 7y - 7z$

4. $2p^2 - p - 2p + 1$

Objective 2: Restricted Values of a Rational Expression
Identify the restricted values.

5. $\dfrac{5}{k+2}$

6. $\dfrac{-3}{h-4}$

7. $\dfrac{x-4}{x^2+9}$

Objective 3: Least Common Denominator
Identify the least common denominator for the pair of expressions.

8. $\dfrac{4}{w^2-3w+2}$ and $\dfrac{w}{w^2-4}$

9. $\dfrac{-3}{24y+8}$ and $\dfrac{5}{18y+6}$

Objective 4: Definition of $a^{\frac{1}{n}}$ **and** $a^{\frac{m}{n}}$

Convert the expressions to radical form and simplify.

10. $144^{\frac{1}{2}}$ 12. $81^{-\frac{3}{2}}$

11. $243^{\frac{3}{5}}$ 13. $(-8)^{\frac{1}{3}}$

Objective 5: Converting Between Rational Exponents and Radical Notation

Convert each expression to radical notation.

14. $q^{\frac{2}{3}}$ 15. $t^{\frac{3}{5}}$ 16. $6y^{\frac{3}{4}}$

Write each expression using rational exponents rather than radical notation.

17. $\sqrt[3]{x}$ 18. $\sqrt[3]{y^2}$

Prerequisite ReviewLinear, Compound, and Absolute Value Inequalities   Section 1.7

This worksheet will cover the following:
Objective 1: Set-Builder Notation and Interval Notation
Objective 2: Linear Equations Involving Multiple Steps

Objective 1: Set-Builder Notation and Interval Notation
Express each of the following in set-builder notation and interval notation.

1.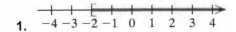

2.

3.

Objective 2: Linear Equations Involving Multiple Steps
Solve each equation.

4. $\dfrac{1}{2}t - 2 = 3$

7. $-\dfrac{5}{9}w + \dfrac{11}{12} = \dfrac{23}{36}$

5. $2k - 9 = -8$

8. $\dfrac{1}{2}(2c - 4) + 3 = \dfrac{1}{3}(6c + 3)$

6. $\dfrac{3}{7}x - 5 = \dfrac{24}{7}x + 7$

9. $\dfrac{2x + 1}{3} + \dfrac{x - 1}{3} = 5$

Prerequisite ReviewLinear, Compound, and Absolute Value Inequalities **Section 1.7**

10. $\dfrac{4y-2}{5} - \dfrac{y+4}{5} = -3$

13. $7y - 3(2y+5) = 7 - (10-10y)$

11. $\dfrac{z-7}{4} = \dfrac{6z-1}{8} - 2$

14. $4 + 2\big[8-(6+x)\big] = -2(x-1)-4+x$

12. $\dfrac{2x-1}{4} + \dfrac{3x+2}{6} = 2$

Chapter 1 – Prerequisite Review Worksheet - ANSWERS

Section 1.1
1. $10t - 44w$
2. $23y$
3. $-\dfrac{9}{5}p + \dfrac{5}{2}$
4. $3k + 11$
5. $a^2 + 10a + 25$
6. $a^2 - 6a + 9$
7. $16q^2 + 24q + 9$
8. $(x+4)(3x+1)$
9. $(p-2)(2p+1)$
10. $(2n+3)(3n-1)$
11. $(w-2)(4w-1)$
12. 36
13. $12a^2b$
14. $(w+3)(w-8)(w+1)$
15. $40(2r+1)$
16. $(x-3)(x+7)$

Section 1.2
1. $x+5$
2. $x - 5,682,080$
3. $10x$
4. $2x$
5. $3x - 20$
6. $x - 117$
7. $\dfrac{132}{4} = \dfrac{x}{9}$
8. $\dfrac{12}{10} = \dfrac{x}{60}$

Section 1.3
1. $3\sqrt{7}$
2. $2\sqrt{5}$
3. $5\sqrt{2}$
4. $15\sqrt{2}$
5. $4\sqrt{6}$

Section 1.5

6. $4\sqrt{5}$
7. $-30\sqrt{3}$
8. $2\sqrt{3}$
9. $7\sqrt{6}$
10. $y^2 - 6$
11. $3 - x^2$
12. $-\dfrac{\sqrt{7}}{7}$
13. $\dfrac{3\sqrt{2}}{2}$
14. $\dfrac{\sqrt{3}}{6}$
15. $\dfrac{4\sqrt{2} - 12}{-7}$
16. $\dfrac{24 + 6\sqrt{3}}{13}$

Section 1.4
1. $x^2 - 16x + 64$
2. $y^2 + 6y + 9$
3. $(x-8)^2$
4. $(y+3)^2$
5. $2(a-5)^2$
6. $3(t+3)^2$
7. $(5m-3n)^2$
8. $(3h-2)(3h+1)$
9. $\dfrac{10-\sqrt{3}}{2}$ or $5 - \dfrac{\sqrt{3}}{2}$
10. $7 - 5\sqrt{2}$
11. $\dfrac{9+4\sqrt{3}}{3}$ or $3 + \dfrac{4}{3}\sqrt{3}$

1. $33\,cm^2$

Chapter 1 – Prerequisite Review Worksheet - ANSWERS

2. $119 \, ft^2$
3. $60 \, m^2$
4. $180 \, in^3$
5. $156 \, in^3$
6. $\dfrac{391}{16} cm^3 \text{ or } 24.4375 \, cm^3$
7. $5 \, m$
8. $15 \, inches$
9. $12 \, yd$
10. $6 \, km^2$
11. $10.12 \, km^2$
12. $40 \, mi^2$

Section 1.6

1. $(2a-b)(4a+3c)$
2. $(y-z)(x+7)$
3. $(a+6)(5a-2)$
4. $(2p-1)(p-1)$
5. $k = -2$
6. $h = 4$
7. *no restricted values*
8. $(w-1)(w-2)(w+2)$
9. $24(3y+1)$
10. 12
11. 27
12. $\dfrac{1}{729}$
13. -2

14. $\sqrt[3]{q^2}$
15. $\sqrt[5]{t^3}$
16. $6\sqrt[4]{y^3}$
17. $x^{\frac{1}{3}}$
18. $y^{\frac{2}{3}}$

Section 1.7

1. $\{x \mid x \ge -2\}; \ [-2, \infty)$
2. $\{x \mid x < -3\}; \ (-\infty, -3)$
3. $\{x \mid -3 < x \le 1\}; \ (-3, 1]$
4. $t = 10$
5. $k = \dfrac{1}{2}$
6. $x = -4$
7. $w = \dfrac{1}{2}$
8. $c = 0$
9. $x = 5$
10. $y = -3$
11. $z = \dfrac{3}{4}$
12. $x = \dfrac{23}{12}$
13. $y = -\dfrac{4}{3}$
14. $x = 10$

Functions and Relations

Prerequisite Review   The Rectangular Coordinate System and Graphing Utilities   **Section 2.1**

This worksheet will cover the following:

Objective 1: Simplify Radicals

Objective 2: Pythagorean Theorem

Objective 3: Solve Literal Equations for an Indicated Variable

Objective 4: Evaluate Expressions for a Given Variable

Objective 1: Simplify Radicals

Simplify the radicals.

1. $\sqrt{28}$

3. $\sqrt{75}$

2. $\sqrt{63}$

4. $5\sqrt{8}$

Objective 2: Pythagorean Theorem

5. Given a right triangle with a leg of 6 feet and hypotenuse of length 10 feet, find the length of the unknown leg.

6. Given a right triangle with legs of 7 cm and 24 cm, find the length of the hypotenuse.

Objective 3: Solve Literal Equations for an Indicated Variable

Solve for the indicated variable.

7. $3x + y = -19$, *for y*

8. $2x + 3y = 6$, *for y*

9. $7x + 3y = 1$, *for* y

11. $Q = \dfrac{x+y}{2}$, *for* y

10. $4x - 3y = 12$, *for* y

Objective 4: Evaluate Expressions for a Given Variable

Evaluate the given expressions.

12. $x^2 + 5x + 1$ *for* $x = -3$

14. $y^2 + 8y - 4$ *for* $y = -7$

13. $x^2 - 2x + 7$ *for* $x = 4$

Prerequisite Review   **Circles**   **Section 2.2**

This worksheet will cover the following:
Objective 1: Completing the Square
Objective 2: Distance Formula
Objective 3: Special Case Products

Objective 1: Completing the Square

Find the value of n so that the expression is a perfect square trinomial.

1. $x^2 + 12x + n$

2. $t^2 + 8t + n$

3. $v^2 - 18v + n$

4. $a^2 - 7a + n$

5. $b^2 + \dfrac{2}{5}b + n$

6. $p^2 - \dfrac{2}{3}p + n$

Objective 2: Distance Formula

Use the distance formula to find the distance between the two points.

7. $(4, 13)$ *and* $(4, -6)$

8. $(-2, 5)$ *and* $(-2, 9)$

9. $(-2, 7)$ *and* $(4, -5)$

10. $(1, 10)$ *and* $(-2, 4)$

Prerequisite Review   **Circles**   **Section 2.2**

Objective 3: Special Case Products

Square the binomials.

11. $(k-4)^2$

12. $(h+3)^2$

13. $(2c+5)^2$

14. $(5d-9)^2$

Prerequisite Review   **Functions and Relations**   **Section 2.3**

This worksheet will cover the following:
Objective 1: Solve Quadratic Equations by Using the Square Root Property
Objective 2: Solve Quadratic Equations
Objective 3: Solve Linear Inequalities
Objective 4: Solve Absolute Value Equations
Objective 5: x- and y- Intercepts

Objective 1: Solve Quadratic Equations by Using the Square Root Property
Solve the equations by using the square root property.

1. $k^2 - 7 = 0$ 2. $6p^2 - 4 = 68$ 3. $15 = 4 + 3w^2$

Objective 2: Solve Quadratic Equations
Solve the quadratic equations by the method of your choice.

4. $7k^2 - 9k - 10 = 0$ 5. $2m^2 + 13m = 24$ 6. $10x^2 + 7x - 3 = 0$

Objective 3: Solve Linear Inequalities
Solve the inequality. Write the solution set in interval notation.

7. $-2x - 4 \le 11$ 8. $4n + 2 < 6n + 8$

Objective 4: Solve Absolute Value Equations
Solve.

9. $|x| + 5 = 11$ 10. $|2x - 4| = 5$

Prerequisite Review   **Functions and Relations**   **Section 2.3**

11. $|3x + 7| = 10$

12. $|2y + 1| + 4 = 10$

Objective 5: x- and y- Intercepts

13. Given the equation $4x + 5y = 0$
    a. Find the x-intercept.
    b. Find the y-intercept.

14. Given the equation $3x + 6y = 12$
    a. Find the x-intercept.
    b. Find the y-intercept.

Prerequisite Review   Linear Equations in Two Variables and Linear Functions   Section 2.4

This worksheet will cover the following:

Objective 1: Finding the x- and y-intercepts of a Graph Defined by $y = f(x)$

Objective 2: Solve Literal Equations for an Indicated Variable

Objective 3: Solve Linear Inequalities

Objective 4: Evaluating Functions

Objective 1: Finding the x- and y-intercepts of a Graph Defined by $y = f(x)$

Find the x- and y-intercepts and graph the function.

1. $f(x) = 2x + 6$

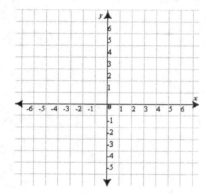

2. $f(x) = -4x + 3$

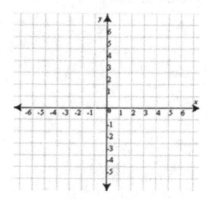

Objective 2: Solve Literal Equations for an Indicated Variable

Solve the following equations for y.

3. $x = y - z$

5. $-3x + 5y = 15$

4. $8x + 2y = 10$

6. $6x - 3y = 4$

Prerequisite Review   **Linear Equations in Two Variables and Linear Functions**   **Section 2.4**

Objective 3: Solve Linear Inequalities

Solve the inequality. Write the solution set in interval notation.

7. $12 > 7x + 9$

9. $2w - 1 \leq 5w + 8$

8. $3t \geq 7t - 35$

10. $5y + 7 > 3y + 15$

Objective 4: Evaluating Functions

Given the function defined by $g(x) = -x^2 + 4x + 7$, find the following:

11. $g(-1)$

12. $g(2)$

13. $g(0)$

14. $g(-3)$

Prerequisite Review   **Applications of Linear Equations and Modeling**   Section 2.5

This worksheet will cover the following:
Objective 1: Slope-Intercept Form of a Linear Equation
Objective 2: Writing an Equation of a Line Using Slope-Intercept Form
Objective 3: Slope
Objective 4: Writing a Linear Model Given a Fixed Value and a Rate of Change

Objective 1: Slope-Intercept Form of a Linear Equation

Write an equation of the line given the following information. Write the answer in slope-intercept form.

1. The slope is 6, and the line passes through the point $(1, -2)$.

2. The slope is 10, and the y-intercept is $(0, -19)$.

3. The slope is -4, and the line passes through the point $(4, -3)$.

4. The slope is $\dfrac{1}{2}$, and the line passes through the point $(-4, -5)$.

Objective 2: Writing an Equation of a Line Using Slope-Intercept Form

Identify the slope and the y-intercept, if they exist.

5. $8x + 2y = 10$

6. $y = -2x + 3$

7. $3x + 2y = 9$

8. $3x - y = 5$

9. $2x - 5y = 4$

10. $7x - 3y = -6$

Prerequisite Review   **Applications of Linear Equations and Modeling**   **Section 2.5**

Objective 3: Slope

Find the slope of the line that passes through the two points.

11. $(-2,3)$ *and* $(1,-6)$ 13. $(1,5)$ *and* $(-4,2)$ 15. $(2,-7)$ *and* $(2,5)$

12. $(2,4)$ *and* $(-4,2)$ 14. $(5,3)$ *and* $(-2,3)$

Objective 4: Writing a Linear Model Given a Fixed Value and a Rate of Change

16. A stack of posters to advertise a production by the theater department costs \$19.95 plus \$1.50 per poster at the printer. Write a linear equation to compute the cost, *c*, of buying *x* posters.

Prerequisite Review   **Transformations of Graphs**   **Section 2.6**

This worksheet will cover the following:
Objective 1: Graphing Linear Equations in Two Variables
Objective 2: Graphing Horizontal and Vertical Lines

Objective 1: Graphing Linear Equations in Two Variables
Objective 2: Graphing Horizontal and Vertical Lines
Graph each equation.

1. $y = -3x - 3$

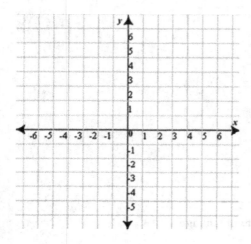

3. $4x + 2y = 8$

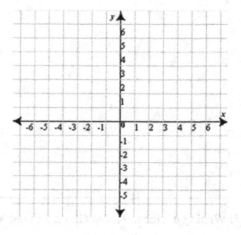

4. $y = -\dfrac{3}{5}x - 2$

2. $2x - 3y = 6$

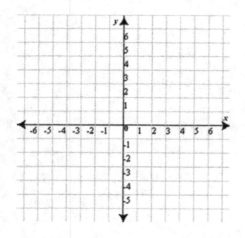

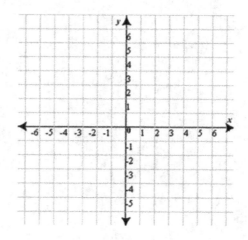

5. $y = -\dfrac{1}{2}x + 3$

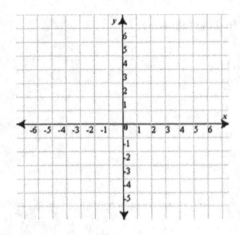

7. $x = 4$

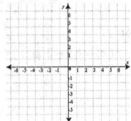

8. $x = -1$

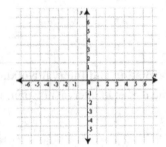

9. $y = 2$

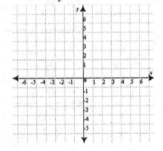

6. $y = \dfrac{1}{4}x - 2$

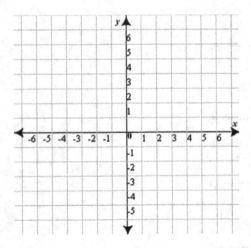

10. $y = -3$

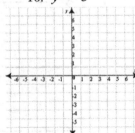

Prerequisite Review   Analyzing Graphs of Functions and Piecewise-Defined Functions   Section 2.7

This worksheet will cover the following:
Objective 1: Function Notation
Objective 2: Set-Builder Notation and Interval Notation

Objective 1: Function Notation
Given the functions defined by $f(x) = 6x - 2$ and $g(x) = -x^2 - 4x + 1$, find the following.

1. $f(t)$

3. $f(a)$

2. $g(a)$

4. $f(-a)$

Objective 2: Set-Builder Notation and Interval Notation
Graph the solution and write the set in interval notation.

5. $\{x \mid x \geq 6\}$

$\longleftarrow \hspace{3cm} \longrightarrow$

6. $\{x \mid x \leq 2.1\}$

$\longleftarrow \hspace{3cm} \longrightarrow$

7. $\left\{x \mid x > \dfrac{7}{3}\right\}$

$\longleftarrow \hspace{3cm} \longrightarrow$

8. $\{x \mid x < -5\}$

$\longleftarrow \hspace{3cm} \longrightarrow$

9. $\{x \mid x \geq -2\}$

$\longleftarrow \hspace{3cm} \longrightarrow$

10. $\{x \mid -3 < x \leq 1\}$

$\longleftarrow \hspace{3cm} \longrightarrow$

Prerequisite Review   Algebra of Functions and Function Compositions   Section 2.8

This worksheet will cover the following:
Objective 1: Domain of a Function
Objective 2: Function Notation

Objective 1: Domain of a Function
Find the domain. Write the answers in interval notation.

1. $k(x) = \dfrac{x-3}{x+6}$

6. $p(t) = 2t^2 + t - 1$

2. $g(t) = \dfrac{t-7}{t}$

7. $q(t) = t^3 + t - 1$

8. $k(x) = \dfrac{3}{\sqrt{x+2}}$

3. $f(a) = \sqrt{a-3}$

4. $g(a) = \sqrt{a+2}$

9. $f(x) = \dfrac{5}{\sqrt{4-x}}$

5. $n(x) = \sqrt{12-6x}$

Objective 2: Function Notation

10. Given $f(x) = 6x - 2$, find $f(x+1)$.

11. Given $g(x) = 3x + 5$, find $g(w+4)$.

12. Given $h(x) = x^2 + 3x - 1$, find $h(x-2)$.

Chapter 2 – Prerequisite Review Notebook - ANSWERS

Section 2.1

1. $2\sqrt{7}$
2. $3\sqrt{7}$
3. $5\sqrt{3}$
4. $10\sqrt{2}$
5. The 3rd side is 8 feet.
6. The hypotenuse is 25 cm.
7. $y = -3x - 19$
8. $y = \dfrac{-2x + 6}{3}$
9. $y = \dfrac{-7x + 1}{3}$
10. $y = \dfrac{-4x + 12}{-3}$ or $y = \dfrac{4x - 12}{3}$
11. $y = 2Q - x$
12. -5
13. 15
14. -11

Section 2.2

1. 36
2. 16
3. 81
4. $\dfrac{49}{4}$
5. $\dfrac{1}{25}$
6. $\dfrac{1}{9}$
7. 19
8. 4
9. $6\sqrt{5}$
10. $3\sqrt{5}$
11. $k^2 - 8k + 16$
12. $h^2 + 6h + 9$
13. $4c^2 + 20c + 25$
14. $25d^2 - 90d + 81$

Section 2.3

1. $\pm\sqrt{7}$
2. $\pm 2\sqrt{3}$
3. $\pm\dfrac{\sqrt{33}}{3}$
4. $\left\{2, -\dfrac{5}{7}\right\}$
5. $\left\{-8, \dfrac{3}{2}\right\}$
6. $\left\{-1, \dfrac{3}{10}\right\}$
7. $\left[-\dfrac{15}{2}, \infty\right)$
8. $(-3, \infty)$
9. $\{-6, 6\}$
10. $\left\{\dfrac{9}{2}, -\dfrac{1}{2}\right\}$
11. $\left\{1, -\dfrac{17}{3}\right\}$
12. $\left\{\dfrac{5}{2}, -\dfrac{7}{2}\right\}$

13a. $(0, 0)$
13b. $(0, 0)$
14a. $(4, 0)$
14b. $(0, 2)$

Section 2.4

1. $(0, 6)$ and $(-3, 0)$
2. $(0, 3)$ and $\left(\dfrac{3}{4}, 0\right)$
3. $y = x + z$
4. $y = -4x + 5$
5. $y = \dfrac{3}{5}x + 3$

Chapter 2 – Prerequisite Review Notebook - ANSWERS

6. $y = 2x - \dfrac{4}{3}$

7. $\left(-\infty, \dfrac{3}{7}\right)$

8. $\left(-\infty, \dfrac{35}{4}\right]$

9. $[-3, \infty)$

10. $(4, \infty)$

11. 2

12. 11

13. 7

14. -14

Section 2.5

1. $y = 6x - 8$

2. $y = 10x - 19$

3. $y = -4x + 13$

4. $y = \dfrac{1}{2}x - 3$

5. $m = -4; \ (0, 5)$

6. $m = -2; \ (0, 3)$

7. $m = -\dfrac{3}{2}; \left(0, \dfrac{9}{2}\right)$

8. $m = 3; \ (0, -5)$

9. $m = \dfrac{2}{5}; \left(0, -\dfrac{4}{5}\right)$

10. $m = \dfrac{7}{3}; \ (0, 2)$

11. $m = -3$

12. $m = \dfrac{1}{3}$

13. $m = \dfrac{3}{5}$

14. $m = 0$

15. Slope is undefined

16. $C = 19.95 + 1.50x$

Section 2.6

1.

2.

3.

4.

5.

6.

7.

Chapter 2 – Prerequisite Review Notebook - ANSWERS

8.

9.

10.

8. $(-\infty, -5)$

9. $[-2, \infty)$

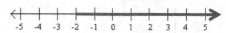

10. $(-3, 1]$

Section 2.8

1. $(-\infty, -6) \cup (-6, \infty)$
2. $(-\infty, 0) \cup (0, \infty)$
3. $[3, \infty)$
4. $[-2, \infty)$
5. $(-\infty, 2]$
6. $(-\infty, \infty)$
7. $(-\infty, \infty)$
8. $(-2, \infty)$
9. $(-\infty, 4)$
10. $6x + 4$
11. $3w + 17$
12. $x^2 - x - 3$

Section 2.7

1. $6t - 2$
2. $-a^2 - 4a + 1$
3. $6a - 2$
4. $-6a - 2$
5. $[6, \infty)$

6. $(-\infty, 2.1]$

7. $\left(\dfrac{7}{3}, \infty\right)$

Polynomial and Rational Functions

Prerequisite Review   Quadratic Functions and Applications   Section 3.1

This worksheet will cover the following:
Objective 1: Solving Quadratic Equations
Objective 2: Function Notation and Finding the x- and y- intercepts
Objective 3: Solving Quadratic Equations by Using the Square Root Property
Objective 4: Evaluating Functions
Objective 5: Domain and Range of a Function

Objective 1: Solving Quadratic Equations
Solve the equations.

1. $(x-5)(x+1)=0$ 2. $p^2-2p-15=0$ 3. $w^2-10w+16=0$

Objective 2: Function Notation and finding the x- and y- intercepts
Given the function $f(x)=x^2+4x+3$

4. Find the values of x for which $f(x)=0$.

5. Find $f(0)$.

Objective 3: Solving Quadratic Equations by Using the Square Root Property
Solve using the square root property.

6. $x^2=100$ 7. $-2m^2=50$ 8. $(p-5)^2=9$

Find the value of n so that the expression is a perfect square trinomial.

9. x^2-6x+n 10. t^2+8t+n

Prerequisite Review   Quadratic Functions and Applications   Section 3.1

Solve by completing the square and applying the square root property.

11. $t^2 + 8t + 15 = 0$

12. $x^2 + 6x = -16$

Objective 4: Evaluating Functions

Consider the functions defined by $f(x) = 6x - 2$ *and* $g(x) = -x^2 - 4x + 1$. For exercises 13-15, find the following.

13. $g(2)$

14. $g(0)$

15. $f(-6)$

Objective 5: Domain and Range of a Function

The graph of $y = f(x)$ is given.

16. Write the domain of f.

17. Write the range of f.

The graph of $y = H(x)$ is given.

18. Write the domain of H.

19. Write the range of H.

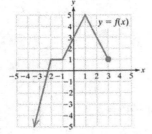

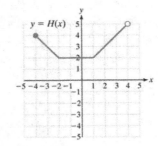

Prerequisite Review   **Introduction to Polynomial Functions**   **Section 3.2**

This worksheet will cover the following:

Objective 1: Solve Equations by Factoring

Objective 2: Use Transformations to Graph Functions

Objective 1: Solve Equations by Factoring

Solve each equation.

1. $x(3x+1)(x+1)=0$

2. $x(x-4)(2x+3)=0$

3. $-3x(x+7)(3x-5)=0$

4. $3n^3+4n^2+n=0$

5. $x^3-16x=0$

6. $0=2m^3-5m^2-12m$

7. $3d^3-6d^2=24d$

8. $w^3+5w^2-9w-45=0$

Prerequisite Review   **Introduction to Polynomial Functions**   **Section 3.2**

Objective 2: Use Transformations to Graph Functions

For exercises 9-14, match the function with its graph.

9. $k(x) = (x-3)^2$

10. $m(x) = x^2 - 4$

11. $p(x) = (x+1)^2 - 3$

12. $n(x) = -(x-2)^2 + 3$

13. $f(x) = \frac{1}{4}x^2$

14. $f(x) = -\frac{1}{4}x^2$

a.

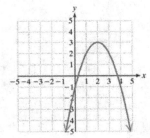

d.

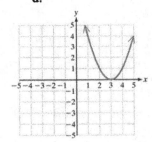

b.

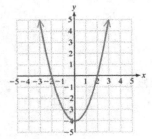

e.

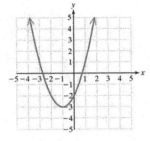

c.

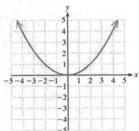

f.

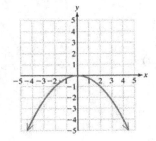

Prerequisite Review   Division of Polynomials and the Remainder and Factor Theorems   Section 3.3

This worksheet will cover the following:
Objective 1: Multiplication of Complex Numbers
Objective 2: Verify by Substitution that Given Values of x are Solutions to Equations
Objective 3: Solving Quadratic Equations by Using the Quadratic Formula

Objective 1: Multiplication of Complex Numbers
Evaluate the following and write the answer in standard form, $a + bi$.

1. $(8i)(3i)$

5. $(4+5i)^2$

2. $6i(1-3i)$

6. $(3-2i)^2$

3. $-i(3+4i)$

4. $(4+7i)(2-3i)$

Objective 2: Verify by Substitution that Given Values of x are Solutions to Equations

Verify by substitution that given values of x are solutions.

7. $x^2 - 6x + 10 = 0$

    a. $3 + i$ b. $3 - i$

8. $y^2 + 4y + 6 = 0$

    a. $-2 + i\sqrt{2}$ b. $-2 - i\sqrt{2}$

Objective 3: Solving Quadratic Equations by Using the Quadratic Formula

Solve the equations by using the quadratic formula.

9. $x^2 - 4x + 5 = 0$ 10. $a^2 + 10 = -2a$

This worksheet will cover the following:

Objective 1: Evaluating Special Products with Complex Numbers

Objective 1: Evaluating Special Products with Complex Numbers

Perform the indicated operations. Write the answers in standard form, $a + bi$.

1. $(7i)(-7i)$ 2. $(4i)(-4i)$ 3. $(-10i)(10i)$

4. $(10 - 4i)(10 + 4i)$ 5. $\left(\sqrt{3} + 4i\right)\left(\sqrt{3} - 4i\right)$ 6. $\left(\sqrt{2} + i\sqrt{3}\right)\left(\sqrt{2} - i\sqrt{3}\right)$

7. $(2 + i)^2 + (2 - i)^2$ 8. $(4 - 3i)^2 + (4 + 3i)^2$

Prerequisite Review   **Rational Functions**   **Section 3.5**

This worksheet will cover the following:

Objective 1: Restricted Values of a Rational Equation

Objective 2: Simplifying Rational Expressions

Objective 1: Restricted Values of a Rational Equation

Identify the restricted values.

1. $\dfrac{5}{k+2}$

2. $\dfrac{x+5}{(2x-5)(x+8)}$

3. $\dfrac{m+12}{m^2+5m+6}$

4. $\dfrac{x-4}{2x}$

Objective 2: Simplifying Rational Expressions

Simplify the following rational expressions.

5. $\dfrac{(p-3)(p+5)}{(p+5)(p+4)}$

6. $\dfrac{5}{20a-25}$

7. $\dfrac{x-5}{5-x}$

8. $\dfrac{4q-4}{12-12q}$

9. $\dfrac{6p^2 + 12p}{2pq - 4p}$

11. $\dfrac{ac - ad + 2bc - 2bd}{2ac + ad + 4bc + 2bd}$

10. $\dfrac{2x + 4}{x^2 - 3x - 10}$

12. $\dfrac{5x^3 + 4x^2 - 45x - 36}{x^2 - 9}$

For the following exercises identify the restricted values and simplify the rational expression.

13. $\dfrac{3y + 6}{6y + 12}$

14. $\dfrac{8n - 20}{4n^2 - 25}$

Prerequisite Review   **Polynomial and Rational Inequalities**   **Section 3.6**

This worksheet will cover the following:

Objective 1: Interval Notation

Objective 2: Solving Linear Inequalities

Objective 3: Adding Rational Expressions

Objective 1: Interval Notation

Graph each inequality and write the solution set in interval notation.

1. $x \geq 6$

interval notation: _____

2. $-2 < x \leq 7$

interval notation: _____

Objective 2: Solving Linear Inequalities

Solve the inequality. Write the solution set in interval notation.

3. $3q - 7 > 2q + 3$

6. $3(x+1) - 2 \leq \dfrac{1}{2}(4x - 8)$

4. $-12 > 7x + 9$

7. $3w - 7 \geq 17 \quad or \quad w < 1$

5. $8 - 6(x - 3) > -4x + 12$

Objective 3: Adding Rational Expressions

Add the rational expressions.

8. $\dfrac{1}{3} + \dfrac{7}{3}$

12. $\dfrac{m-1}{m+1} + \dfrac{4}{2m+5}$

9. $\dfrac{2a}{a+2} + \dfrac{4}{a+2}$

13. $\dfrac{6}{a-5} + 7b$

10. $\dfrac{n^2}{n+5} + \dfrac{7n+10}{n+5}$

14. $a+1+\dfrac{1}{a-1}$

11. $\dfrac{8}{11} + \dfrac{y}{4}$

Prerequisite Review   **Variation**   Section 3.7

This worksheet will cover the following:
Objective 1: Solving Literal Equations for an Indicated Variable
Objective 2: Solving Proportions

Objective 1: Solving Literal Equations for an Indicated Variable
Solve for the indicated variable.

1. $P = a + b + c$ for a

2. $d = rt$ for r

3. $PV = nrt$ for t

4. $P_1 V_1 = P_2 V_2$ for V_1

5. $-2x - y = 9$ for x

6. $ax + by = c$ for x

7. $A = P(1 + rt)$ for t

8. $P = 2(L + w)$ for L

9. $Q = \dfrac{x + y}{2}$ for y

Objective 2: Solving Proportions

Solve the proportion.

10. $\dfrac{8}{5} = \dfrac{152}{p}$

11. $\dfrac{19}{76} = \dfrac{z}{4}$

12. $\dfrac{16}{1.3} = \dfrac{30}{p}$

13. $\dfrac{y+1}{2y} = \dfrac{2}{3}$

Chapter 3 – Prerequisite Review Worksheets - ANSWERS

Section 3.1

1. $x = 5, x = -1$
2. $p = 5, p = -3$
3. $w = 8, w = 2$
4. $x = -1, x = -3$
5. $f(0) = 3$
6. $\{\pm 10\}$
7. $\{\pm 5i\}$
8. $\{8, 2\}$
9. $n = 9$
10. $n = 16$
11. $\{-3, -5\}$
12. $\{-3 \pm i\sqrt{7}\}$
13. -11
14. 1
15. -38
16. $(-\infty, 3]$
17. $(-\infty, 5]$
18. $[-4, 4)$
19. $[2, 5)$

Section 3.2

1. $\left\{0, -\dfrac{1}{3}, -1\right\}$
2. $\left\{0, 4, -\dfrac{3}{2}\right\}$
3. $\left\{0, -7, \dfrac{5}{3}\right\}$
4. $\left\{0, -\dfrac{1}{3}, -1\right\}$
5. $\{0, -4, 4\}$

6. $\left\{0, 4, -\dfrac{3}{2}\right\}$
7. $\{0, 4, -2\}$
8. $\{-3, 3, -5\}$
9. d
10. b
11. e
12. a
13. c
14. f

Section 3.3

1. $-24 + 0i$
2. $18 + 6i$
3. $4 - 3i$
4. $29 + 2i$
5. $-9 + 40i$
6. $5 - 12i$
7. VERIFY
8. VERIFY
9. $2 \pm i$
10. $-1 \pm 3i$

Section 3.4

1. $49 + 0i$
2. $16 + 0i$
3. $100 + 0i$
4. $116 + 0i$
5. $19 + 0i$
6. $5 + 0i$
7. $6 + 0i$
8. $14 + 0i$

Chapter 3 – Prerequisite Review Worksheets - ANSWERS

Section 3.5

1. $k = -2$

2. $x = \dfrac{5}{2}, x = -8$

3. $m = -3, m = -2$

4. $x = 0$

5. $\dfrac{p-3}{p+4}$

6. $\dfrac{1}{4a-5}$

7. -1

8. $-\dfrac{1}{3}$

9. $\dfrac{3(p+2)}{q-2}$

10. $\dfrac{2}{x-5}$

11. $\dfrac{c-d}{2c+d}$

12. $5x+4$

13. $y = -2$; $\dfrac{1}{2}$

14. $n = -\dfrac{5}{2}, \dfrac{5}{2}$; $\dfrac{4}{2n+5}$

Section 3.6

1. $[6, \infty)$

2. $(-2, 7]$

3. $(10, \infty)$

4. $(-\infty, -3)$

5. $(-\infty, 7)$

6. $(-\infty, -5]$

7. $(-\infty, 1) \cup [8, \infty)$

8. $\dfrac{8}{3}$

9. 2

10. $n + 2$

11. $\dfrac{32 + 11y}{44}$

12. $\dfrac{2m^2 + 7m - 1}{(m+1)(2m+5)}$

13. $\dfrac{6 + 7ab - 35b}{a - 5}$

14. $\dfrac{a^2}{a-1}$

Section 3.7

1. $a = P - b - c$

2. $r = \dfrac{d}{t}$

3. $t = \dfrac{PV}{nr}$

4. $V_1 = \dfrac{P_2 V_2}{P_1}$

5. $x = \dfrac{y+9}{-2}$

6. $x = \dfrac{c - by}{a}$

7. $t = \dfrac{A-P}{\Pr} = \dfrac{A}{\Pr} - \dfrac{1}{r}$

8. $L = \dfrac{P}{2} - w$

9. $y = 2Q - x$

10. $p = 95$

11. $z = 1$

12. $p = 2.4375$

13. $y = 3$

Exponential and Logarithmic Functions

Prerequisite Review   Inverse Functions   Section 4.1

This worksheet will cover the following:
Objective 1: Domain of a Function
Objective 2: Composition of Functions

Objective 1: Domain of a Function
Find the domain. Write the answers in interval notation.

1. $k(x) = \dfrac{x-3}{x+6}$

2. $m(x) = \dfrac{x-1}{x-4}$

3. $f(t) = \dfrac{5}{t}$

4. $n(p) = \dfrac{p+8}{p^2+2}$

5. $h(t) = \sqrt{t+7}$

6. $k(t) = \sqrt{t-5}$

7. $g(a) = \sqrt{a+2}$

8. $m(x) = \sqrt{1-2x}$

9. $f(x) = x+6$

Prerequisite Review   **Inverse Functions**   **Section 4.1**

Objective 2: Composition of Functions

Given the functions f, g, h and $k,$ find the indicated functions.

$$f(x) = x + 4 \qquad g(x) = 2x^2 + 4x \qquad h(x) = x^2 + 1 \qquad k(x) = \frac{1}{x}$$

10. $(f \circ g)(x)$

13. $(k \circ h)(x)$

11. $(f \circ k)(x)$

14. $(g \circ k)(x)$

12. $(k \circ f)(x)$

This worksheet will cover the following:

Objective 1: Determining the Domain and Range of a Function

Objective 2: Transformations of Graphs

Objective 3: Applying Notation Describing Infinite Behavior of a Function

Objective 1: Determining the Domain and Range of a Function

Determine the domain and range of each graph.

1. Domain: Range:

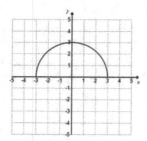

2. Domain: Range:

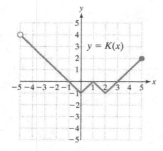

3. Domain: Range:

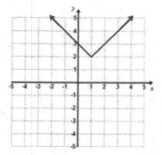

4. Domain: Range:

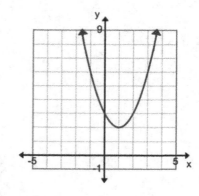

5. Domain: Range:

6. Domain: Range:

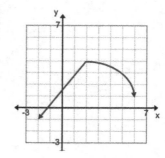

Prerequisite Review   **Exponential Functions**   **Section 4.2**

Objective 2: Transformations of Graphs

Describe the transformations of the functions below from the parent function of $f(x) = x^2$.

7. $f(x) = (x+4)^2$

8. $f(x) = -(x+3)^2 - 2$

Objective 3: Applying Notation Describing Infinite Behavior of a Function

Refer to the graph of the function and complete the statements.

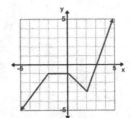

9.

   a. The graph is decreasing over the interval(s) _____

   b. The graph is increasing over the interval(s)_____

10. Refer to the graph of the function and complete the statements.

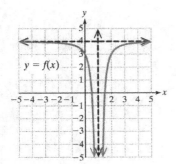

   a. As $x \to -\infty, f(x) \to$ _____

   b. $x \to 1^-, f(x) \to$ _____

   c. $x \to 1^+, f(x) \to$ _____

   d. $x \to \infty, f(x) \to$ _____

   e. The graph is increasing over the interval(s)_____

   f. The graph is decreasing over the interval(s)_____

   g. The domain is _____

   h. The range is _____

This worksheet will cover the following:

Objective 1: Converting Between Rational Exponents and Radical Notation

Objective 2: Properties of Rational Exponents

Objective 3: Solving Polynomial Inequalities

Objective 1: Converting Between Rational Exponents and Radical Notation

Objective 2: Properties of Rational Exponents

Convert each expression to radical form and simplify.

1. $8^{\frac{2}{3}}$

2. $100^{\frac{5}{2}}$

3. $144^{\frac{1}{2}}$

4. $25^{\frac{3}{2}}$

5. $16^{\frac{3}{4}}$

6. $-16^{\frac{3}{4}}$

7. $(-16)^{\frac{3}{4}}$

8. $4^{\frac{3}{2}}$

9. $4^{-\frac{3}{2}}$

10. $(-8)^{\frac{1}{3}}$

11. $25^{-\frac{1}{2}}$

12. $64^{-\frac{3}{2}}$

Prerequisite Review   **Logarithmic Functions**   **Section 4.3**

Objective 3: Solving Polynomial Inequalities

Solve the polynomial inequality. Write the answer in interval notation.

13. $(t-7)(t-1)<0$

15. $x^2+x\leq 6$

14. $w^2+20w+64\geq 0$

16. $c^2-25<0$

Prerequisite Review   **Properties of Logarithms**   **Section 4.4**

This worksheet will cover the following:
Objective 1: Simplifying Expressions with Exponents

Objective 1: Simplifying Expressions with Exponents
Use the properties of exponents to simplify the expression.

1. $z^5 z^3$

2. $a a^8$

3. $\left(\dfrac{2}{3} m^{13} n^8\right)\left(24 m^7 n^2\right)$

4. $(10y)(2y^3)$

5. $\dfrac{w^7}{w^6}$

6. $\dfrac{w^{12} w^2}{w^4 w^5}$

7. $\dfrac{-12 s^2 t u^3}{4 s u^2}$

8. $(y^7)^2$

9. $(a^2 a^4)^6$

10. $(5w)^2$

11. $(-5xyz)^2$

12. $(-k^6)^3$

13. $\left(\dfrac{2c^3 d^4}{3c^2 d}\right)^2$

18. $\left(\dfrac{2}{7}\right)^{-3}$

14. $x^{-8} x^4$

19. $7y^{-1}$

15. $\dfrac{p^3}{p^9}$

20. $(3z)^{-1}$

21. $\left(\dfrac{4m^{10} n^4}{2m^{12} n^{-2}}\right)^{-1}$

16. $\dfrac{u^{-2}}{u^{-6}}$

17. $\dfrac{p^3}{p^{-5}}$

This worksheet will cover the following:
Objective 1: Linear Equations Involving Multiple Steps
Objective 2: Solving Equations by Factoring
Objective 3: Solving Quadratic Equations by Using the Quadratic Formula
Objective 4: Solving Rational Equations
Objective 5: Solving Radical Equations Involving One Radical

Objective 1: Linear Equations Involving Multiple Steps
Solve each equation.

1. $6(3x+2)-10=-4$

2. $5(4+p)=3(3p-1)-9$

Objective 2: Solving Equations by Factoring
Solve each equation.

3. $2c(c-8)=-30$

5. $x(2x+5)-1=2x^2+3x+2$

4. $3q(q-3)=12$

Objective 3: Solving Quadratic Equations by Using the Quadratic Formula
Solve by using the quadratic formula.

6. $x^2+11x-12=0$

7. $k^2+4=6k$

Prerequisite Review   Exponential and Logarithmic Equations and Applications   Section 4.5

Objective 4: Solving Rational Equations

Solve each equation.

8. $\dfrac{5x}{x+1} + \dfrac{1}{x} = 5$

10. $\dfrac{18}{m^2 - 3m} + 2 = \dfrac{6}{m-3}$

11. $30k^{-2} - 23k^{-1} + 2 = 0$

9. $7 + \dfrac{20}{z} = \dfrac{3}{z^2}$

Objective 5: Solving Radical Equations Involving One Radical

Solve the Equations.

12. $\sqrt{x} + 4 = 6$

14. $\sqrt{x^2 + 5} = x + 1$

13. $\sqrt{5y + 1} = 4$

15. $\sqrt{2n + 29} + 3 = n$

Prerequisite Review   Modeling with Exponential and Logarithmic Functions   Section 4.6

This worksheet will cover the following:

Objective 1: Solving Literal Equations for an Indicated Variable

Objective 2: Evaluating Functions

Objective 1: Solving Literal Equations for an Indicated Variable

Solve for the indicated variable.

1. $A = lw$ for l

6. $C = 2\pi r$ for r

2. $3x + 5y = 15$ for y

7. $A = \pi r^2$ for $r, \quad r > 0$

3. $\dfrac{1}{4}x - \dfrac{2}{3}y = 2$ for y

8. $V = \dfrac{1}{3}x^2 h$ for $x, \quad x > 0$

4. $V = \dfrac{1}{3}Bh$ for B

9. $a^2 + b^2 + c^2 = d^2$ for $c, \quad c > 0$

5. $P = I^2 R$ for R

Prerequisite Review   Modeling with Exponential and Logarithmic Functions   Section 4.6

Objective 2: Evaluating Functions

For the following, find the function values given $f(x) = 6x^2 - 4$.

10. $f(0)$

13. $f(b)$

14. $f(-2)$

11. $f(1)$

12. $f(-1)$

Given $h(x) = \dfrac{3}{x-3}$, find the following.

15. $h(-3)$

17. $h(2)$

18. $h(5)$

16. $h(0)$

Chapter 4 – Prerequisite Review Worksheets - ANSWERS

Section 4.1

1. $(-\infty,-6)\cup(-6,\infty)$
2. $(-\infty,4)\cup(4,\infty)$
3. $(-\infty,0)\cup(0,\infty)$
4. $(-\infty,\infty)$
5. $[-7,\infty)$
6. $[5,\infty)$
7. $[-2,\infty)$
8. $\left(-\infty,\dfrac{1}{2}\right]$
9. $(-\infty,\infty)$
10. $2x^2+4x+4$
11. $\dfrac{1}{x}+4; \, x\neq 0$
12. $\dfrac{1}{x+4}; \, x\neq -4$
13. $\dfrac{1}{x^2+1}$
14. $\dfrac{2}{x^2}+\dfrac{4}{x}; \, x\neq 0$

Section 4.2

1. *domain* $(-5,5]$; *range* $[-1,4)$: $(-\infty,4)$
2. *domain* $[-3,3]$; *range* $[0,3]$
3. *domain* $(-\infty,\infty)$; *range* $[2,\infty)$
4. *domain* $[-2,\infty)$; *range* $[0,\infty)$
5. *domain* $(-\infty,\infty)$; *range* $[2,\infty)$
6. *domain* $(-\infty,\infty)$; *range* $(-\infty,4]$
7. Left 4
8. Left 3; reflected over x-axis; down 2
9. $a:(0,2)$ $b:(-\infty,-2)\cup(2,\infty)$
10.
   a. 4
   b. $-\infty$
   c. $-\infty$
   d. 4

e. $(1,\infty)$
f. $(-\infty,1)$
g. $(-\infty,1)\cup(1,\infty)$
h. $(-\infty,4)$

Section 4.3

1. 4
2. 100,000
3. 12
4. 125
5. 8
6. -8
7. *not a real number*
8. 8
9. $\dfrac{1}{8}$
10. -2
11. $\dfrac{1}{5}$
12. $\dfrac{1}{512}$
13. $(1,7)$
14. $(-\infty,-16]\cup[-4,\infty)$
15. $[-3,2]$
16. $(-5,5)$

Section 4.4

1. z^8
2. a^9
3. $16m^{20}n^{10}$
4. $20y^4$
5. w
6. w^5
7. $-3stu$
8. y^{14}
9. a^{36}
10. $25w^2$
11. $25x^2y^2z^2$
12. $-k^{18}$

Chapter 4 – Prerequisite Review Worksheets - ANSWERS

13. $\dfrac{4}{9}c^2 d^6$

14. $\dfrac{1}{x^4}$

15. $\dfrac{1}{p^6}$

16. u^4

17. p^8

18. $\dfrac{343}{8}$

19. $\dfrac{7}{y}$

20. $\dfrac{1}{3z}$

21. $\dfrac{m^2}{2n^6}$

Section 4.5

1. $x = -\dfrac{1}{3}$

2. $p = 8$

3. $\{3,5\}$

4. $\{4,-1\}$

5. $x = \dfrac{3}{2}$

6. $\{1,-12\}$

7. $\{3 \pm \sqrt{5}\}$

8. $\left\{\dfrac{1}{4}\right\}$

9. $\left\{\dfrac{1}{7},-3\right\}$

10. $\{\ \}$; 3 *does not check*

11. $\left\{\dfrac{3}{2},10\right\}$

12. $\{4\}$

13. $\{3\}$

14. $\{2\}$

15. $\{10\}$; -2 *does not check*

Section 4.6

1. $l = \dfrac{A}{w}$

2. $y = -\dfrac{3}{5}x + 3$

3. $y = \dfrac{3}{8}x - 3$

4. $B = \dfrac{3V}{h}$

5. $R = \dfrac{P}{I^2}$

6. $r = \dfrac{C}{2\pi}$

7. $r = \sqrt{\dfrac{A}{\pi}} = \dfrac{\sqrt{A\pi}}{\pi}$

8. $x = \sqrt{\dfrac{3V}{h}}$ *or* $x = \dfrac{\sqrt{3Vh}}{h}$

9. $c = \sqrt{d^2 - a^2 - b^2}$

10. -4

11. 2

12. 2

13. $6b^2 - 4$

14. 20

15. $-\dfrac{1}{2}$

16. -1

17. -3

18. $\dfrac{3}{2}$

Systems of Equations and Inequalities

This worksheet will cover the following:
Objective 1: Linear Equations Involving Multiple Steps
Objective 2: Conditional Equations, Identities, and Contradictions
Objective 3: Graphing Equations and Identifying x- and y-intercepts
Objective 4: Graphing Equations and Identifying the slope and y-intercept

Objective 1: Linear Equations Involving Multiple Steps
Solve each equation.

1. $7x + 3 = 6(x - 2)$

4. $17(s + 3) = 4(s - 10) + 13$

2. $2(q + 3) = 4q + q - 9$

5. $5 - 3(x + 2) = 5$

3. $3.4x - 2.5 = 2.8x + 3.5$

6. $0.40(y + 10) - 0.60(y + 2) = 2$

Objective 2: Conditional Equations, Identities, and Contradictions
Solve each equation.

7. $5h + 4 = 5(h + 1) - 1$

9. $2(x + 2) - 3 = 2x + 1$

8. $2(k - 7) = 2k - 13$

10. $10(2n + 1) - 6 = 20(n - 1) + 12$

Prerequisite ReviewSystems of Linear Equations in Two Variables and Applications　Section 5.1

Objective 3: Graphing Equations and Identifying x- and y-intercepts
Graph the equation and identify the x- and y-intercepts.

11. $2x+8=y$

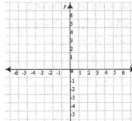

12. $5x+2y=5$

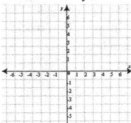

Objective 4: Graphing Equations and Identifying the slope and y-intercept
Graph the equation and identify the slope and the y-intercept.

13. $2x=-4y+6$

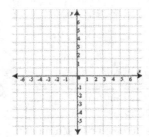

14. $x-2y=6$

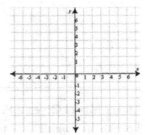

Prerequisite Review   Systems of Linear Equations in Three Variables and Applications   Section 5.2

This worksheet will cover the following:
Objective 1: Applications Involving Simple Interest
Objective 2: Writing a Linear Model Given a Fixed Value and a Rate of Change
Objective 3: Linear Equations Involving Fractions

Objective 1: Applications Involving Simple Interest

1. Anna invested $3000 in an account paying 8% simple interest. How much interest will she earn in 3 ½ years?

3. How much interest will Diane have to pay if she borrows $4000 for 3 years at a simple interest rate of 4%?

2. Andrea borrowed $3250 for 2 years at 6% simple interest. How much total money will she have to pay back?

Objective 2: Writing a Linear Model Given a Fixed Value and a Rate of Change

4. Andrea has a cell phone plan with a local telephone company. Her bill is determined each month by a $39.99 flat fee plus $0.20 for each text message sent or received. Write a linear model to compute the monthly cost, y, of Andrea's cell phone bill if x text messages are sent or received.

5. The cost to rent a storage space is $90 per month plus a nonrefundable deposit of $105. Write a linear equation to compute the cost, y, of renting a storage space for x months.

6. A bakery that specializes in bread rents a booth at a flea market. The daily cost to rent the booth is $100. Each loaf of bread costs the bakery $0.80 to produce. Write a linear equation to compute the total cost, y, for 1 day if x loaves of bread are produced.

Objective 3: Linear Equations Involving Fractions

Solve each equation.

7. $\dfrac{2x+1}{3}+\dfrac{x-1}{3}=5$

10. $\dfrac{2k+5}{4}=2-\dfrac{k+2}{3}$

8. $\dfrac{3w-2}{6}=1-\dfrac{w-1}{3}$

11. $\dfrac{3d-4}{6}+1=\dfrac{d+1}{8}$

9. $\dfrac{x+3}{3}-\dfrac{x-1}{2}=4$

Prerequisite Review   Partial Fraction Decomposition   Section 5.3

This worksheet will cover the following:
Objective 1: Factoring by Grouping
Objective 2: Factoring Perfect Square Trinomials
Objective 3: Addition and Subtraction of Rational Expressions
Objective 4: Using Long Division to Divide Polynomials
Objective 5: Solving Rational Equations

Objective 1: Factoring by Grouping
Factor completely.

1. $8a^2 - 4ab + 6ac - 3bc$ 2. $4y^2 + 8y + 7y + 14$ 3. $6y^2 - 2y - 9y + 3$

Objective 2: Factoring Perfect Square Trinomials
Factor Completely.

4. $x^2 + 18x + 81$ 5. $25z^2 - 20z + 4$ 6. $49a^2 + 42ab + 9b^2$

Objective 3: Addition and Subtraction of Rational Expressions
Add or subtract the expressions.

7. $\dfrac{5b}{b+4} + \dfrac{20}{b+4}$ 8. $\dfrac{5}{x} + \dfrac{3}{x+2}$ 9. $\dfrac{4}{y-3} + \dfrac{y}{y-5}$

Objective 4: Using Long Division to Divide Polynomials

Divide the polynomials using long division.

10. $\dfrac{18y^2 + 9y - 20}{3y + 4}$ 11. $\dfrac{3y^3 - 7y^2 - 4y + 3}{y - 3}$ 12. $\dfrac{18x^3 + 7x + 12}{3x - 2}$

Objective 5: Solving Rational Equations

Solve the equations.

13. $\dfrac{a+1}{a} = 1 + \dfrac{a-2}{2a}$ 14. $\dfrac{2t}{t+2} - 2 = \dfrac{t-8}{t+2}$ 15. $\dfrac{2}{x} + \dfrac{1}{2} = \dfrac{1}{4}$

This worksheet will cover the following:

Objective 1: Graph Quadratic Functions in the Form $f(x) = ax^2 + bx + c$

Objective 2: Graph Circles

Objective 3: Graph Radical Functions

Objective 4: Solve Logarithmic and Exponential Equations

Objective 1: Graph Quadratic Functions in the Form $f(x) = ax^2 + bx + c$

Graph the functions.

1. $f(x) = x^2 + 4x + 3$

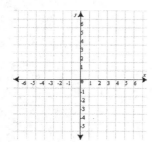

2. $s(x) = -2x^2 - 12x - 19$

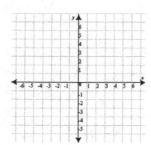

Objective 2: Graph Circles

Identify the center and radius of the circle and then graph the circle.

3. $x^2 + (y - 2)^2 = 4$

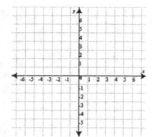

4. $(x - 3)^2 + (y + 1)^2 = 16$

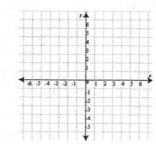

Prerequisite Review   Systems of Nonlinear Equations in Two Variables   Section 5.4

Objective 3: Graph Radical Functions

Graph the functions. Write the domain in interval notation.

5. $f(x) = \sqrt{x+3}$

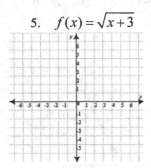

7. $f(x) = \sqrt{x} - 1$

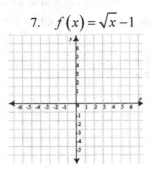

8. $f(x) = \sqrt{x-4}$

6. $f(x) = \sqrt{x} + 2$

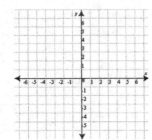

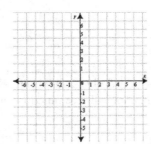

Objective 4: Solve Logarithmic and Exponential Equations

Solve the logarithmic and exponential equations.

9. $\ln x = 19$

11. $5^x = 625$

13. $4^{2x-1} = 64$

10. $\log_5(4y+1) = 1$

12. $2^x = 32$

Prerequisite Review   Inequalities and Systems of Inequalities in Two Variables   Section 5.5

This worksheet will cover the following:
Objective 1: Solving Systems of Linear Equations and Inequalities by Graphing

Objective 1: Solving Systems of Linear Equations and Inequalities by Graphing

1. Use the graphs to solve the equation and inequalities. Write the solutions to the inequalities in interval notation. (Note: you should solve the functions for y)

    a. $-x+4=2x-5$
    b. $-x+4<2x-5$
    c. $-x+4\geq 2x-5$

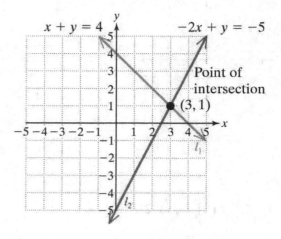

2. Use the graphs to solve the equation and inequalities. Write the solutions to the inequalities in interval notation. (Note: These functions are solved for y.)

    a. $\dfrac{3}{2}x+3=\dfrac{1}{2}x+1$

    b. $\dfrac{3}{2}x+3<\dfrac{1}{2}x+1$

    c. $\dfrac{3}{2}x+3\geq\dfrac{1}{2}x+1$

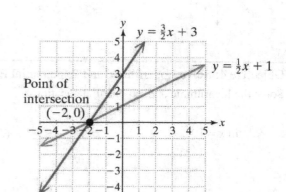

Prerequisite Review   Linear Programming   Section 5.6

This worksheet will cover the following:
Objective 1: Writing a Linear Model Given a Fixed Value and a Rate of Change
Objective 2: Create Linear Functions to Model Data

Objective 1: Writing a Linear Model Given a Fixed Value and a Rate of Change

1. For a recent year, children's admission to the Minnesota State Fair was $8. Ride tickets were $0.75 each.
    a. Write an equation that represents the cost y (in $) to be admitted to the fair and to purchase x ride tickets.
    b. What is the y-intercept and what does it mean in the context of this problem?

2. A water purification company charges $20 per month and a $55 installation fee.
    a. Write a linear equation to compute the total cost, y, of renting this system for x months.
    b. What is the y-intercept and what does it mean in the context of this problem?
    c. Use the equation from part (a) to determine the total cost to rent the system for 9 months.

3. A small cleaning company has a fixed monthly cost of $700 and a variable cost of $8 per service call.
    a. Write a linear equation to compute the total cost, y, of making x service calls in one month.
    b. What is the y-intercept and what does it mean in the context of this problem?
    c. Use the equation from part (a) to determine the total cost of making 80 service calls.

Objective 2: Create Linear Functions to Model Data

4. A family plan for a cell phone has a monthly base price of $99 plus $12.99 for each additional family member added beyond the primary account holder.

    a. Write a linear function to model the monthly cost $C(x)$ (in $) of a family plan for x additional family members added.

    b. Evaluate $C(4)$ and interpret the meaning in the context of this problem.

5. A speeding ticket is $100 plus $5 for every 1 mph over the speed limit.

    a. Write a linear function to model the cost $S(x)$ (in $) of a speeding ticket for a person caught driving x mph over the speed limit.

    b. Evaluate $S(15)$ and interpret the meaning in the context of this problem.

Chapter 5 – Prerequisite Review Worksheets - ANSWERS

Section 5.1

1. $\{-15\}$
2. $\{5\}$
3. $\{10\}$
4. $\{-6\}$
5. $\{-2\}$
6. $\{4\}$
7. $\square$
8. $\{\ \}$
9. $\square$
10. $\{\ \}$
11. $(0,8)(-4,0)$

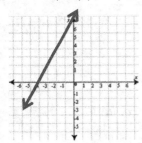

12. $\left(0,\dfrac{5}{2}\right),(1,0)$

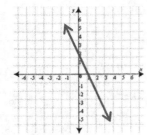

13. $m=-\dfrac{1}{2};\left(0,\dfrac{3}{2}\right)$

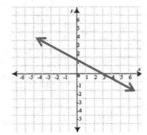

14. $m=\dfrac{1}{2};(0,-3)$

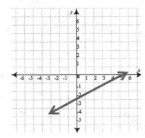

Section 5.2

1. $840
2. $3640
3. $480
4. $y=0.20x+39.99$
5. $y=90x+105$
6. $y=0.80x+100$
7. $\{5\}$
8. $\{2\}$
9. $\{-15\}$
10. $\left\{\dfrac{1}{10}\right\}$
11. $\left\{-\dfrac{5}{9}\right\}$

Chapter 5 – Prerequisite Review Worksheets - ANSWERS

Section 5.3

1. $(2a-b)(4a+3c)$
2. $(y+2)(4y+7)$
3. $(3y-1)(2y-3)$
4. $(x+9)^2$
5. $(5z-2)^2$
6. $(7a+3b)^2$
7. 5
8. $\dfrac{2(4x+5)}{x(x+2)}$
9. $\dfrac{(y+5)(y-4)}{(y-3)(y-5)}$
10. $6y-5$
11. $3y^2+2y+2+\dfrac{9}{y-3}$
12. $6x^2+4x+5+\dfrac{22}{3x-2}$
13. $\{4\}$
14. $\{4\}$
15. $\{-8\}$

2.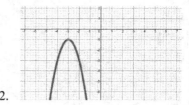

3. *center* $(0,2)$; *radius* 2

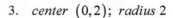

4. *center* $(3,-1)$; *radius* 4

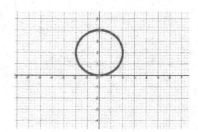

5. $[-3,\infty)$

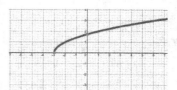

Section 5.4

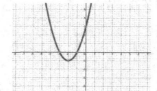

1.

Chapter 5 – Prerequisite Review Worksheets - ANSWERS

6. $[0,\infty)$

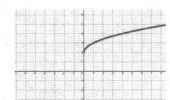

7. $[0,\infty)$

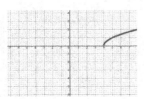

8. $[4,\infty)$

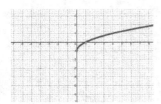

9. $\{e^{19}\}$

10. $\{1\}$

11. $\{4\}$

12. $\{5\}$

13. $\{2\}$

Section 5.5

1.
    a. $\{3\}$
    b. $(3,\infty)$
    c. $(-\infty,3]$

2.
    a. $\{-2\}$
    b. $(-\infty,-2)$
    c. $[-2,\infty)$

Section 5.6

1.
    a. $y=0.75x+8$
    b. There is a flat fee of $8 to get into the park.

2.
    a. $y=20x+55$
    b. There is a one-time fee for installation of $55.
    c. $235

3.
    a. $y=8x+700$
    b. The fixed cost for the company is $700 per month.
    c. $1340

4.
    a. $C(x)=12.99x+99$
    b. $C(4)=150.96$. The total monthly cost of the plan with 4 additional family members beyond the primary account holder is $150.96.

5.
    a. $S(x)=5x+100$
    b. $S(15)=175$. A person caught speeding 15 mph over the speed limit will have a ticket cost of $175.

Matrices and Determinants
and Applications

Prerequisite Review   Solving Systems of Linear Equations Using Matrices   Section 6.1

This worksheet will cover the following:

Objective 1: Solve Linear Equations

Objective 2: Applications Involving Simple Interest

Objective 3: Set Up a partial Fraction Decomposition

Objective 1: Solve Linear Equations

Solve each equation.

1. $7n - 4 = 17$

2. $5n + 3 = 9$

3. $5 - 3x = 32$

Objective 2: Applications Involving Simple Interest

4. Stacey borrowed $15,000 at 7% interest rate for 10 years. What is the interest she will pay?

6. If Jessica borrows $30,000 for 15 years at 4%, what is the amount of interest she will pay?

5. How much interest will Jeff have to pay if he borrows $4000 for 3 years at a simple interest rate of 5%?

Prerequisite Review   Solving Systems of Linear Equations Using Matrices   Section 6.1

Objective 3: Set Up a partial Fraction Decomposition

Set up the form for the partial fraction decomposition for the given rational expressions.

7. $\dfrac{-x-37}{(x+4)(2x-3)}$

8. $\dfrac{y-12}{y^2+3y}$

9. $\dfrac{6w-7}{w^2+w-6}$

10. $\dfrac{17x^2-7x+18}{7x^3+42x}$

Prerequisite Review   Inconsistent Systems and Dependent Equations   Section 6.2

This worksheet will cover the following:
Objective 1: Solve Literal Equations for a Specified Variable
Objective 2: Test for Symmetry

Objective 1: Solve Literal Equations for a Specified Variable
Solve for the indicated variable.

1. $7x + 2y = 8$ *for y*

4. $-2x - y = 9$ *for x*

2. $3x + 5y = 15$ *for y*

5. $6x - 3y = 4$ *for y*

3. $x - y = 5$ *for x*

6. $x - 6y = -10$ *for x*

Objective 2: Test for Symmetry

7. A graph of an equation is symmetric with respect to the _____-axis if replacing x by $-x$ results in an equivalent equation.

8. A graph of an equation is symmetric with respect to the _____-axis if replacing y by $-y$ results in an equivalent equation.

Determine whether the graph of the equation is symmetric with respect to the x-axis or y-axis.

9. $y = x^2 + 3$

11. $x = -|y| - 4$

10. $y = -|x| - 4$

12. $x = y^2 + 3$

Prerequisite Review   **Operations on Matrices**   **Section 6.3**

This worksheet will cover the following:
Objective 1: Inverse Properties of Real Numbers
Objective 2: Commutative Properties of Real Numbers
Objective 3: Solve Linear Equations

Objective 1: Inverse Properties of Real Numbers
Identify the additive inverse of the following.

   1. 11   2. -2 3. 25   4. -7

Objective 2: Commutative Properties of Real Numbers
Apply the commutative property of addition to the following.

   5. $(-8) + y$ 7. $a + b$

   6. $x + 7$ 8. $-23 + z$

Rewrite each expression using addition. Then apply the commutative property of addition.

   9. $x - 3$ 10. $4p - 9$ 11. $3m - 12$

Objective 3: Solve Linear Equations
Solve the equations.

   12. $3x + 7 = 13$ 14. $2 - 7s = -19$

   13. $\dfrac{x}{4} + 9 = 6$ 15. $8 + 3x = 5$

Prerequisite Review   Inverse Matrices and Matrix Equations   Section 6.4

This worksheet will cover the following:
Objective 1: Properties of Real Numbers

Objective 1: Properties of Real Numbers
Match the statement with the property that describes it.

    a.   Identity property of addition
    b.   Identity property of multiplication
    c.   Inverse property of addition
    d.   Inverse property of multiplication

1. $6 \cdot \dfrac{1}{6} = 1$

2. $18 \cdot 1 = 18$

3. $3 + 0 = 3$

4. $5 + (-5) = 0$

5. $\dfrac{1}{11} \cdot 11 = 1$

6. $(-17) + 17 = 0$

7. $0 + 9 = 9$

8. $1 \cdot 23 = 23$

Prerequisite Review   **Determinants and Cramer's Rule**   **Section 6.5**

This worksheet will cover the following:
Objective 1: Exponential Expressions
Objective 2: Write Equations of Lines

Objective 1: Exponential Expressions
Simplify.

1. $(-6)^2$

2. $(-10)^2$

3. -6^2

4. -10^2

5. $\left(-\dfrac{3}{5}\right)^3$

6. $\left(-\dfrac{3}{5}\right)^2$

7. $-\left(\dfrac{3}{5}\right)^2$

8. $(-5)^2$

9. -5^2

10. $\left(-\dfrac{1}{2}\right)^3$

11. -2^3

12. $(-2)^3$

Objective 2: Write Equations of Lines
Write an equation of the line having the given conditions. Write the answer in slope-intercept form (if possible).

13. The line passes through the points $(-2,-6)$ *and* $(1,0)$.

14. The line passes through the points $(-2,5)$ *and* $(0,1)$.

15. The line passes through the points $(1,-3)$ *and* $(-7,2)$.

Chapter 6 – Prerequisite Review Worksheets - ANSWERS

Section 6.1

1. $\{3\}$
2. $\left\{\dfrac{6}{5}\right\}$
3. $\{-9\}$
4. $10,500
5. $600
6. $18,000
7. $\dfrac{A}{x+4}+\dfrac{B}{2x-3}$
8. $\dfrac{A}{y}+\dfrac{B}{y+3}$
9. $\dfrac{A}{w-2}+\dfrac{B}{w+3}$
10. $\dfrac{A}{7x}+\dfrac{Bx+C}{x^2+6}$

Section 6.2

1. $y=-\dfrac{7}{2}x+4$
2. $y=-\dfrac{3}{5}x+3$
3. $x=y+5$
4. $x=\dfrac{y+9}{-2}\ \ or\ \ x=-\dfrac{1}{2}y-\dfrac{9}{2}$
5. $y=2x-\dfrac{4}{3}$
6. $x=6y-10$
7. y
8. x
9. y-axis
10. y-axis
11. x-axis
12. x-axis

Section 6.3

1. -11
2. 2
3. -25
4. 7
5. $y+(-8)$
6. $7+x$
7. $b+a$
8. $z+(-23)$
9. $x+(-3);\ \ -3+x$
10. $4p+(-9);\ \ -9+4p$
11. $3m+(-12);\ \ -12+3m$
12. $\{2\}$
13. $\{-12\}$
14. $\{3\}$
15. $\{-1\}$

Section 6.4

1. d
2. b
3. a
4. c
5. d
6. c
7. a
8. b

Chapter 6 – Prerequisite Review Worksheets - ANSWERS

Section 6.5

1. 36
2. 100
3. −36
4. −100
5. $-\dfrac{27}{125}$
6. $\dfrac{9}{25}$
7. $-\dfrac{9}{25}$
8. 25
9. −25
10. $-\dfrac{1}{8}$
11. −8
12. −8
13. $y = 2x - 2$
14. $y = -2x + 1$
15. $y = -\dfrac{5}{8}x - \dfrac{19}{8}$

Analytic Geometry

Prerequisite Review   The Ellipse   Section 7.1

This worksheet will cover the following:
Objective 1: Circles
Objective 2: Factoring Perfect Square Trinomials
Objective 3: Writing an Equation of a Circle

Objective 1: Circles
Determine the center and radius of the circle.

1. $x^2 + y^2 = 25$

2. $x^2 + y^2 = 6$

3. $(x-4)^2 + (y+2)^2 = 9$

4. $x^2 + (y-2)^2 = 4$

5. $(x-3)^2 + y^2 = 8$

6. $\left(x + \dfrac{4}{5}\right)^2 + y^2 = \dfrac{64}{25}$

Objective 2: Factoring Perfect Square Trinomials
Find the value of n so that the expression is a perfect square trinomial. Then factor the trinomial.

7. $x^2 + 12x + n$

8. $x^2 - 26x + n$

9. $x^2 + 11x + n$

10. $v^2 - 18v + n$

Prerequisite Review   **The Ellipse**   **Section 7.1**

Objective 3: Writing an Equation of a Circle

Identify the center and radius of the circle. Complete the square, if necessary.

11. $x^2 + y^2 - 2x - 6y - 26 = 0$ 13. $x^2 + y^2 - 6y + 5 = 0$

12. $x^2 + y^2 + 4x - 8y + 16 = 0$ 14. $x^2 + 2x + y^2 - 15 = 0$

Prerequisite Review   The Hyperbola   Section 7.2

This worksheet will cover the following:
Objective 1: Distance Formula
Objective 2: Writing an Equation of a Line Using Slope-Intercept Form

Objective 1: Distance Formula
Use the distance formula to find the distance between the two points.

1. $(-2, 7)$ *and* $(4, -5)$ 2. $(1, 10)$ *and* $(-2, 4)$ 3. $(0, 5)$ *and* $(-3, 8)$

Objective 2: Writing an Equation of a Line Using Slope-Intercept Form
Write an equation of the line satisfying the given conditions. Write the answer in slope-intercept form.

4. The line passes through the point $(-3, 1)$ and has a slope of 2.

5. The slope is 10, and the y-intercept is $(0, 5)$.

6. The slope is 6, and the line passes through the point $(1, -2)$.

Prerequisite Review   **The Hyperbola**   **Section 7.2**

7. The line passes through $(2,-1)$ *and* $(0,3)$.

8. The line passes through $(4,-8)$ *and* $(0,-4)$.

9. The line passes through $(3,1)$ *and* $(-3,3)$.

10. The line passes through $(1,3)$ *and* $(-2,-9)$.

Prerequisite Review   The Parabola   Section 7.3

This worksheet will cover the following:
Objective 1: Distance Formula
Objective 2: Writing Equations of Lines Parallel or Perpendicular to Another Line

Objective 1: Distance Formula
Use the distance formula to find the distance between the two points.

1. $(4, 13)$ *and* $(4, -6)$ 2. $(-2, 5)$ *and* $(-2, 9)$ 3. $(-1, -5)$ *and* $(-5, -9)$

Objective 2: Writing Equations of Lines Parallel or Perpendicular to Another Line
Write an equation of the line satisfying the given conditions.

4. Passes through $(2, 7)$ and is parallel to the line $y = 3$.

5. Passes through $(-1, 4)$ and is parallel to the line $x = 10$.

6. Passes through $(5, -2)$ and is perpendicular to the line $x = 4$.

7. Passes through $(3, 1)$ and is perpendicular to the line $y = -3$.

8. Passes through $(8, 6)$ and is parallel to the x-axis.

9. Passes through $(-11, 13)$ and is parallel to the y-axis.

10. Passes through $\left(\dfrac{5}{11}, -\dfrac{3}{4} \right)$ and is perpendicular to the y-axis.

Chapter 7 – Prerequisite Review Worksheets - ANSWERS

Section 7.1

1. $(0,0)$; $r = 5$
2. $(0,0)$; $r = \sqrt{6}$
3. $(4,-2)$; $r = 3$
4. $(0,2)$; $r = 2$
5. $(3,0)$; $r = 2\sqrt{2}$
6. $\left(-\dfrac{4}{5}, 0\right)$; $r = \dfrac{8}{5}$
7. $n = 36$; $(x+6)^2$
8. $n = 169$; $(x-13)^2$
9. $n = \dfrac{121}{4}$; $\left(x + \dfrac{11}{2}\right)^2$
10. $n = 81$; $(n-9)^2$
11. $(1,3)$; $r = 6$
12. $(-2,4)$; $r = 2$
13. $(0,3)$; $r = 2$
14. $(-1,0)$; $r = 4$

Section 7.3

1. 19
2. 4
3. $4\sqrt{2}$
4. $y = 7$
5. $x = -1$
6. $y = -2$
7. $x = 3$
8. $y = 6$
9. $x = -11$
10. $y = -\dfrac{3}{4}$

Section 7.2

1. $6\sqrt{5}$
2. $3\sqrt{5}$
3. $3\sqrt{2}$
4. $y = 2x + 7$
5. $y = 10x + 5$
6. $y = 6x - 8$
7. $y = -2x + 3$
8. $y = -x - 4$
9. $y = -\dfrac{1}{3}x + 2$
10. $y = 4x - 1$

Sequences, Series, Induction, and Probability

Prerequisite Review   Sequences and Series   Section 8.1

This worksheet will cover the following:
Objective 1: Evaluate Functions
Objective 2: Simplify Rational Expressions

Objective 1: Evaluate Functions
Evaluate the function for the given value.

1. $g(x) = \dfrac{7}{x}; \ g(16)$

4. $f(x) = 2x^2 + 3; \ f(4)$

5. $m(x) = 2; \ m(4)$

2. $h(x) = x^2 - 4x; \ h(3)$

3. $h(x) = x^2 - 4x; \ h(-3)$

Objective 2: Simplify Rational Expressions
Simplify the rational expression.

6. $\dfrac{m^7}{m^2}$

9. $\dfrac{x^2(x+7)^8}{x(x+7)^2}$

7. $\dfrac{x^8}{x^{12}}$

10. $\dfrac{(m+2)^3}{(m+2)^7}$

8. $\dfrac{(x+3)^2(x-2)^5}{(x+3)(x-2)^3}$

11. $\dfrac{m^4(m-1)^6}{m^7(m-1)^2}$

Prerequisite Review   Arithmetic Sequences and Series   Section 8.2

This worksheet will cover the following:
Objective 1: Evaluate Functions
Objective 2: Slope and y-intercept of a Line
Objective 3: Solving Systems of Linear Equations

Objective 1: Evaluate Functions

Evaluate the function defined by $g(x) = 2x + 1$ for the given values of x.

1. $g(-2)$ 4. $g(1)$

2. $g(-1)$ 5. $g(2)$

3. $g(0)$

Objective 2: Slope and y-intercept of a Line

Identify the slope and y-intercept, if they exist.

6. $y = \dfrac{3}{4}x - 1$ 9. $y = -x + 6$

                                              10. $3x - y = 5$

7. $y = \dfrac{2}{3}x + 5$

8. $y = -2x + 3$

Prerequisite Review   **Arithmetic Sequences and Series**   **Section 8.2**

Objective 3: Solving Systems of Linear Equations

Solve each system.

11. $\begin{array}{l} 2x - 3y = 11 \\ -4x + 3y = -19 \end{array}$

12. $\begin{array}{l} -2u + 6v = 10 \\ -2u + v = -5 \end{array}$

13. $\begin{array}{l} 5m - 2n = 4 \\ 3m + n = 9 \end{array}$

14. $\begin{array}{l} 0.02x + 0.04y = 0.12 \\ 0.03x - 0.05y = -0.15 \end{array}$

Prerequisite Review   **Geometric Sequences and Series**   **Section 8.3**

This worksheet will cover the following:
Objective 1: Dividing Fractions
Objective 2: Solving Exponential Equations
Objective 3: Evaluating Exponential Expressions
Objective 4: Computing Compound Interest

Objective 1: Dividing Fractions
Divide the fractions.

1. $\dfrac{8}{5} \div \dfrac{3}{10}$

3. $\dfrac{12}{25} \div \dfrac{8}{15}$

2. $\dfrac{12}{13} \div 6$

4. $\dfrac{1}{4} \div 2$

Objective 2: Solving Exponential Equations
Solve the equations.

5. $5^x = 625$

6. $4^x = 16$

7. $3^x = 27$

Objective 3: Evaluating Exponential Expressions

8. For $f(x) = \left(\dfrac{1}{5}\right)^x$ find $f(0), f(1), f(2), f(-1)$, and $f(-2)$.

9. For $g(x) = \left(\dfrac{2}{3}\right)^x$ find $g(0), g(1), g(2), g(-1)$, and $g(-2)$.

10. For $h(x) = 3^x$ find $h(0), h(1), h(-1)$.

Objective 4: Computing Compound Interest

For the following exercise, use the model $A(t) = P\left(1 + \dfrac{r}{n}\right)^{nt}$ for interest compounded n times per year.

11. Suppose an investor deposits $15,000 in a savings account for 8 years at 5% interest. Find the total amount of money in the account for the following compounding options. Round to the nearest dollar.

    a. Compounded annually

    b. Compounded quarterly

    c. Compounded monthly

Prerequisite Review   **Mathematical Induction**   **Section 8.4**

This worksheet will cover the following:
Objective 1: Factoring Out the Greatest Common Factor
Objective 2: Factoring Out a Negative Factor
Objective 3: Factoring Perfect Square Trinomials
Objective 4: Factoring Trinomials by the Trial and Error Method
Objective 5: Addition and Subtraction of Rational Expressions with Different Denominators

---

Objective 1: Factoring Out the Greatest Common Factor
Factor out the GCF.

1. $4p + 12$

2. $x^5 + x^3$

3. $2ab + 4a^3b$

4. $38x^2y - 19x^2y^4$

Objective 2: Factoring Out a Negative Factor
Factor out the opposite of the greatest common factor.

5. $-15p^3 - 30p^2$

6. $-24m^3 - 12m^4$

Objective 3: Factoring Perfect Square Trinomials
Factor each polynomial.

7. $x^2 + 18x + 81$

8. $y^2 - 8y + 16$

9. $25z^2 - 20z + 4$

10. $36p^2 - 24pq + 4q^2$

Objective 4: Factoring Trinomials by the Trial and Error Method

Factor each polynomial.

11. $x^2 - 4x - 12$ 14. $y^2 + 11y + 30$

12. $x^2 + 7x + 12$ 15. $y^2 - 17y + 30$

13. $y^2 - 7y - 30$

Objective 5: Addition and Subtraction of Rational Expressions with Different Denominators

Simplify.

16. $\dfrac{5}{x} + \dfrac{3}{x+2}$ 18. $\dfrac{3a-7}{6a+10} - \dfrac{10}{3a^2+5a}$

17. $\dfrac{2}{c-4} + \dfrac{1}{5c-20}$ 19. $\dfrac{y}{4y+2} + \dfrac{3y}{6y+3}$

Prerequisite Review   **The Binomial Theorem**   **Section 8.5**

This worksheet will cover the following:
Objective 1: Special Case Products: Perfect Square Trinomials
Objective 2: Multiplication Property of Radicals and Perfect Square Trinomials
Objective 3: Cube Binomials

Objective 1: Special Case Products: Perfect Square Trinomials
Multiply and simplify the polynomials.

1. $(a+5)^2$

4. $(2-3b)^2$

2. $(2c+5)^2$

5. $\left(\dfrac{1}{3}x+4\right)^2$

3. $(3t^2-4s)^2$

6. $\left(\dfrac{2}{5}y+3\right)^2$

Objective 2: Multiplication Property of Radicals and Perfect Square Trinomials
Square the radical expression. Assume all variables represent positive real numbers.

7. $\left(\sqrt{d}+3\right)^2$

8. $\left(\sqrt{13}+4\right)^2$

9. $\left(6z-\sqrt{5}\right)^2$

Objective 3: Cube Binomials
Multiply.

10. $(k-4)^3$

11. $(h+3)^3$

12. $(5x+3)^3$

Prerequisite Review   **Principles of Counting**   **Section 8.6**

This worksheet will cover the following:
Objective 1: Factorial Notation

Objective 1: Factorial Notation
Evaluate the expressions.

1. 5!

2. 3!

3. 0!

4. 1!

5. $\dfrac{8!}{4!}$

6. $\dfrac{7!}{5!}$

7. $\dfrac{3!}{0!}$

8. $\dfrac{8!}{3!5!}$

9. $\dfrac{6!}{2!4!}$

10. $\dfrac{4!}{0!4!}$

Prerequisite Review   **Introduction to Probability**   **Section 8.7**

0077836340**This worksheet will cover the following:**
Objective 1: Determine the Union and Intersection of Sets

Objective 1: Determine the Union and Intersection of Sets
Find the union or intersection as indicated, given the following sets:
$A = \{0, 4, 8, 12\}$, $B = \{0, 3, 6, 9, 12\}$, $C = \{-2, 4, 8\}$.

1. $A \cup B$ 3. $A \cup C$ 5. $B \cup C$

2. $A \cap B$ 4. $A \cap C$ 6. $B \cap C$

Find the union or intersection as indicated, given the following sets:
$C = \{x \mid x < 9\}$, $D = \{x \mid x \geq -1\}$, $F = \{x \mid x < -8\}$.

7. $C \cup D$ 9. $C \cup F$ 11. $D \cup F$

8. $C \cap D$ 10. $C \cap F$ 12. $D \cap F$

Chapter 8 – Prerequisite Review Worksheets - ANSWERS

Section 8.1

1. $\dfrac{7}{16}$

2. -3

3. 21

4. 35

5. 2

6. m^5

7. $\dfrac{1}{x^4}$

8. $(x+3)(x-2)^2$

9. $x(x+7)^6$

10. $\dfrac{1}{(m+2)^4}$

11. $\dfrac{(m-1)^4}{m^3}$

Section 8.2

1. -3

2. -1

3. 1

4. 3

5. 5

6. $m=\dfrac{3}{4}; (0,-1)$

7. $m=\dfrac{2}{3}; (0,5)$

8. $m=-2; (0,3)$

9. $m=-1; (0,6)$

10. $m=3; (0,-5)$

11. $\{(4,-1)\}$

12. $\{(4,3)\}$

13. $\{(2,3)\}$

14. $\{(0,3)\}$

Section 8.3

1. $\dfrac{16}{3}$

2. $\dfrac{2}{13}$

3. $\dfrac{9}{10}$

4. $\dfrac{1}{8}$

5. $\{4\}$

6. $\{2\}$

7. $\{3\}$

8. $f(0)=1, f(1)=\dfrac{1}{5}, f(2)=\dfrac{1}{25},$
$f(-1)=5, f(-2)=25$

9. $g(0)=1, g(1)=\dfrac{2}{3}, g(2)=\dfrac{4}{9},$
$g(-1)=\dfrac{3}{2}, g(-2)=\dfrac{9}{4}$

10. $h(0)=1, h(1)=3, h(-1)=\dfrac{1}{3}$

11 a. $\$22,161.83$

    b. $\$22,321.96$

    c. $\$22,358.78$

Section 8.4

1. $4(p+3)$

2. $x^3(x^2+1)$

3. $2ab(1+2a^2)$

4. $19x^2 y(2-y^3)$

5. $-15p^2(p+2)$

6. $-12m^3(2+m)$

7. $(x+9)^2$

Chapter 8 – Prerequisite Review Worksheets - ANSWERS

8. $(y-4)^2$

9. $(5z-2)^2$

10. $(6p-2q)^2$

11. $(x-6)(x+2)$

12. $(x+3)(x+4)$

13. $(y-10)(y+3)$

14. $(y+5)(y+6)$

15. $(y-15)(y-2)$

16. $\dfrac{2(4x+5)}{x(x+2)}$

17. $\dfrac{11}{5(c-4)}$

18. $\dfrac{(a-4)}{2a}$

19. $\dfrac{3y}{2(2y+1)}$

Section 8.5

1. $a^2+10a+25$

2. $4c^2+20c+25$

3. $9t^4-24st^2+16s^2$

4. $4-12b+9b^2$

5. $\dfrac{1}{9}x^2+\dfrac{8}{3}x+16$

6. $\dfrac{4}{25}y^2+\dfrac{12}{5}y+9$

7. $d+6\sqrt{d}+9$

8. $29+8\sqrt{13}$

9. $36z^2-12z\sqrt{5}+5$

10. $k^3-12k^2+48k-64$

11. $h^3+9h^2+27h+27$

12. $125x^3+225x^2+135x+27$

Section 8.6

1. 120

2. 6

3. 1

4. 1

5. 1680

6. 42

7. 6

8. 56

9. 15

10. 1

Section 8.7

1. $\{0,3,4,6,8,9,12\}$

2. $\{0,12\}$

3. $\{-2,0,4,8,12\}$

4. $\{4,8\}$

5. $\{-2,0,3,4,6,8,9,12\}$

6. $\{\ \}$

7. $\varnothing$

8. $\{x\,|\,-1\le x<9\}$

9. $\{x\,|\,x<9\}$

10. $\{x\,|\,x<-8\}$

11. $\{x\,|\,x<-8\ or\ x\ge-1\}$

12. $\{\ \}$